To Karen + Louis
Love from Mum + Dad

Design: Judith Chant and Alison Lee
Recipe Photography: Peter Barry
Jacket and Illustration Artwork: Jane Winton, courtesy of
Bernard Thornton Artists, London
Editors: Jillian Stewart and Kate Cranshaw

CLB 4263
Published by Grange Books, an imprint of Grange Books PLC,
The Grange, Grange Yard, London, SE1 3AG
© 1995 CLB Publishing, Godalming, Surrey, England.
Printed and bound in Singapore
Published 1995
ISBN 1-85627-583-3

THE LITTLE BOOK · OF ·

Thai Cooking

An easy-to-follow guide to creating authentic Thai dishes.

Grange
BOOKS

Introduction

Thai cooking reflects the influences of both the Indian and Chinese cultures. It has drawn on the best elements of both: the characteristically strong and fiery spices of India, and the speedy methods of Chinese cooking. Added to these two elements are Thailand's own distinctive ingredients including coconut, lemon grass, lime, fish sauce and curry paste. The result of these three inputs is a really exciting cuisine that is not difficult to master. It is a healthy cuisine in which fresh vegetables, served raw or only lightly cooked, play a large part. Oil is generally only added in small quantities. Fish and chicken are more frequent components of a meal than are red meats. The cooking methods used in Thai cooking, such as stir-frying, steaming, roasting and barbecuing, are all simple to use at home. Thai cooking is quick to prepare and cook, with many dishes taking only minutes to produce.

As the attractions of Thai cooking have become well known through new restaurants and media publicity, so the necessary ingredients have become more widely available. Coconut is one of the hallmark tastes of Thai cooking and can be achieved in the West with the use of canned coconut milk. Also available is coconut powder which can be made up with water, and blocks of creamed coconut which can be dissolved before use. Lemon grass can be bought fresh in certain supermarkets and Asian foodstores, as can fish sauce and oyster sauce. Other important ingredients, such as green or red chillies, fresh ginger and fresh coriander, have been available for a long time, and are regularly stocked by the larger supermarkets. The most commonly used utensil in Thai cooking is a wok with a lid. Although a frying pan can be used (especially if cooking with electricity), it is worthwhile investing in this inexpensive piece of equipment.

A Thai meal is usually made up of a selection of savoury dishes accompanied by plain boiled rice. The various dishes will include a soup, a couple of meat dishes – maybe a stir-fry and a barbecue, a vegetable dish with sauce, and a noodle dish. The helpings of each dish tend to be relatively small, in order that each one may be savoured. In Thailand, tiny saucerfuls of delectable savoury dishes are sold at street stalls, and one may pick and choose a variety of foods to eat together. Thai food should be presented with a flourish. Each dish should be served with, for example, an adornment of chopped coriander or an exquisitely fashioned spring onion flower. The prettiness of Thai food, together with the ease of general preparation and quickness of cooking, makes it the perfect cuisine for entertaining.

Curry Parcels

MAKES 18

A tasty snack which can be served any time of the day or as a starter.

PREPARATION: 20 mins
COOKING: 30 mins

225g/8oz chicken breasts
2 tbsps oil
1 small onion, finely chopped
225g/8oz cooked potato, diced
1 tbsp green curry paste, see page 28
2 tsps sugar
18 wonton wrappers
Oil for deep-frying

Sweet and Sour Dipping Sauce
120g/4oz cucumber, finely chopped
120g/4oz carrots, peeled and finely chopped
140ml/¼ pint white wine vinegar
60g/2oz sugar
1 tsp chopped fresh coriander

Garnish
Cucumber slices

1. Skin the chicken and chop finely. Heat the oil in a wok and fry the onion and chicken for 3 minutes.

2. Stir in the potato, curry paste and sugar and fry for a few minutes. Remove the chicken mixture to a plate.

Step 4 Place wonton wrappers on tea-towel and spoon a little of the filling into the centre of each wrapper.

3. Combine all the sauce ingredients in a bowl, and stir until the sugar dissolves.

4. Place the wonton wrappers in front of you on a damp tea-towel to prevent them drying out too quickly. Spoon a little of the filling into the centre of each wrapper.

5. Dampen the edges with water. Pull up the edges of the pastry and pinch together, enclosing the filling. Repeat until you have used up all the filling.

6. Heat the oil in a wok and deep-fry a few at a time for 3-4 minutes or until crisp and golden.

7. Drain on kitchen paper. Serve with the sweet and sour dipping sauce. Garnish with cucumber slices.

Coconut Prawn Soup

SERVES 4

Soup is usually served as part of a full Thai meal, but is also served at any time as a snack or meal on its own.

PREPARATION: 20 mins
COOKING: 10 mins

1 stem of lemon grass
225g/8oz raw king prawns
1.1 litres/2 pints fish stock
4 slices galangal
4 Kaffir lime leaves, shredded
2 red or green chillies, chopped
1 tbsp fish sauce
225g/8oz white fish fillets, cut into strips
140ml/¼ pint thick coconut milk

1. Remove the tough outer leaves of the lemon grass and discard, trim ends and thinly slice a piece about 5cm/2 inches long.

2. Peel the prawns discarding everything except the tails.

Step 3 Pull away the dark vein and discard.

3. Pull away the dark vein and discard.

4. Heat the stock until almost boiling, stir in the galangal, lime leaves, lemon grass, chillies and fish sauce. Simmer for 2 minutes.

5. Add the fish fillets and prawns and cook gently for 5 minutes.

6. Stir in the coconut milk and continue cooking until very hot, but do not allow to boil.

Spring Rolls with Sweet Chilli Sauce

MAKES about 12
*Spring rolls have become so popular that they are even available at some supermarket
delicatessens. They are simple to make at home and will taste much better.*

PREPARATION: 20 mins
COOKING: 20 mins

2 tbsps oil
1 clove garlic, crushed
120g/4oz chopped pork
2 carrots, peeled and cut into thin sticks
2 sticks celery, cut into thin sticks
1 red or green chilli, chopped
4 spring onions, sliced
1 tsp grated fresh root ginger
1 tbsp chopped fresh coriander
1 tsp fish sauce
60g/2oz noodles, cooked
About 12 spring roll wrappers
Oil for deep-frying

Sweet Chilli Sauce
120g/4oz canned plums (drained weight),
    pitted
1 tbsp oil
3 red chillies, chopped
1 clove garlic, crushed
1 tsp sugar
2 tbsps vinegar
Fish sauce to taste

Garnish
Fresh coriander leaves

1. Heat the oil in a wok or frying pan and fry
the garlic, pork, carrots, celery and chilli for a
few minutes until the pork is cooked and the
vegetables are beginning to soften.

2. Stir in the spring onions, ginger, coriander,
fish sauce and noodles, and heat through.

3. Place a spring roll wrapper on the work
surface and position a small amount of the
filling across one corner. Roll up, folding in the
corners completely to enclose the filling. Fill
one spring roll at a time and keep the
remaining wrappers covered with a damp tea
towel to prevent them from drying out.

4. Just before serving deep-fry, in batches, for
3-4 minutes until crisp and golden. Drain on
kitchen paper and keep warm.

5. Meanwhile, chop the plums very finely –
this can be done in a food processor.

6. Heat the oil and fry the chilli and garlic for
3 minutes. Stir in the remaining ingredients and
heat through. Serve with the spring rolls,
garnished with fresh coriander.

Beef in Oyster Sauce

SERVES 4
You can make this spicy dish very quickly.

PREPARATION: 10 mins
COOKING: 10 mins

460g/1lb sirloin steak
2 tbsps oil
¼ tsp ground cumin
¼ tsp ground coriander
175g/6oz baby corn cobs
120g/4oz can bamboo shoots, drained
175g/6oz mange tout peas
2 tbsps oyster sauce
2 tsps soft dark brown sugar
140ml/¼ pint beef stock
1 tsp cornflour
1 tbsp fish sauce

Garnish
Spring onion slices

---

1. Cut the beef into thin slices and then into strips.

2. Heat the oil in a wok and fry the beef over a high heat for 5 minutes or until cooked. Stir in the spices and cook for 1 minute.

Step 1 Cut the beef into thin slices and then into strips.

Step 2 Heat the oil in a wok and fry the beef over a high heat for 5 minutes or until cooked.

3. Add the vegetables, then stir in the oyster sauce, sugar and stock, and bring to the boil.

4. Mix the cornflour with the fish sauce and stir into the pan, cooking until the sauce thickens. Sprinkle with slices of spring onion to garnish.

Thai Sweet Sour Fish

SERVES 2

Fish plays a very important part in Thai cuisine especially in the south. It is often fried in a wok and served with a hot sauce, as in this recipe.

PREPARATION: 15 mins
COOKING: 25 mins

---

2 × 460g/1lb whole fish such as pomfret,
    snapper or bream, cleaned
Oil for shallow-frying
4 green chillies, seeded and sliced
2.5 cm/1-inch piece fresh root ginger, peeled
    and cut into thin sticks
2 cloves garlic, crushed
1 carrot, peeled and cut into thin sticks
3 tbsps white wine vinegar
1 tbsp fish sauce
60g/4 tbsps dark soft brown sugar
60ml/4 tbsps fish stock
6 spring onions, shredded
1 tsp cornflour mixed with a little water

---

1. Cut several slashes in each side of the fish. Heat the oil in a wok or frying pan and fry the fish for about 5-10 minutes each side. Remove from the pan and keep warm while preparing the sauce.

2. Wipe out the pan and heat a little more oil in it. Fry the chillies, ginger, garlic and carrot for 3-4 minutes.

Step 2 Fry the chillies, ginger, garlic and carrot for 3-4 minutes.

3. Stir in the vinegar, fish sauce, sugar and stock and bring to the boil. Add the spring onions.

4. Stir the cornflour and water into the wok and cook until sauce thickens. Pour over the fish to serve.

Step 4 Stir the cornflour and water into the wok and cook until sauce thickens.

Barbecued Pork

SERVES 4

Traditionally this dish would be cooked on charcoal burners by the roadside, but it works just as well in the oven.

PREPARATION: 15 mins, plus 1 hour marinating
COOKING: 20 mins

4 cloves garlic, crushed
140ml/¼ pint light soy sauce
60g/2oz soft dark brown sugar
1 tbsp grated fresh root ginger
1 tbsp chopped fresh coriander stems and root
4 star anise or 1 tsp ground anise
Red food colouring (optional)
2 pork fillets
2 tbsps oil
2 shallots, chopped
120g/4oz roasted peanuts, ground
140ml/¼ pint pork or chicken stock
1 tsp cornflour mixed with a little water

Garnish
Kaffir lime leaves and star anise

Step 3 Test pork with a skewer, the juices should run clear.

1. Mix together the garlic, soy, sugar, ginger, coriander, anise, and a few drops of food colouring if wished, to make a marinade.

2. Place the fillets in a shallow dish and add the marinade. Turn the pork over so that it is fully coated in the marinade. Leave to marinate for at least 1 hour, turning once.

3. Remove the meat from the marinade and place on a trivet in a roasting dish. Roast in a preheated oven, 375°F/190°C/Gas Mark 5, for 20 minutes or until pork is cooked. Baste once or twice with the marinade. Test the pork with a skewer, the juices should run clear.

4. Just before the end of the roasting time, heat the oil in a wok and fry the shallots until tender and beginning to brown. Stir in the ground peanuts, the marinade and stock. Cook until simmering, then add the cornflour mixture and cook a little longer until thickened.

5. To serve, slice the pork and pour the sauce over. Garnish with lime leaves and star anise.

Stir-Fried Chicken with Ginger

SERVES 4
A popular Thai dish served in many restaurants.

PREPARATION: 15 mins
COOKING: 10 mins

2 tbsps oil
2 cloves garlic, crushed
2 shallots, chopped
340g/12oz skinned and boned chicken breast,
    cut into thin strips
5 cm/2-inch piece fresh root ginger, peeled and
    cut into shreds
2 Kaffir lime leaves, shredded
60g/2oz whole blanched almonds
120g/4oz long or French beans, cut into
    5 cm/2-inch lengths
1 red pepper, cut into strips
90g/3oz water chestnuts, sliced
3 tbsps fish sauce
1 tbsp sugar

Step 1 Fry the garlic and shallots until beginning to soften.

Step 3 Add the fish sauce.

1. Heat the oil in a wok and fry the garlic and shallots until beginning to soften. Add the chicken and fry until it changes colour.

2. Add the ginger, lime leaves, almonds, beans, pepper and water chestnuts. Stir-fry, tossing the ingredients frequently, for 5 minutes until vegetables are cooked but still crisp.

3. Stir in the fish sauce and sugar and serve with rice or noodles.

Mussaman Curry

SERVES 4
This curry illustrates the Indian influence on some of Thailand's cuisine.

PREPARATION: 25 mins
COOKING: 1 hour

---

4 cardamom pods
½ tsp coriander seeds
½ tsp caraway seeds
2 whole cloves
5 small red chillies, chopped
1 clove garlic, crushed
1 stem lemon grass, roughly chopped
2 spring onions, chopped
¼ tsp grated fresh root ginger
¼ tsp ground nutmeg
1 tbsp oil
680g/1½lb sirloin steak
Oil for shallow-frying
340g/12oz potatoes, peeled and cut into
    chunks
2-3 onions, peeled and cut into wedges
420ml/¾ pint thin coconut milk
2 tbsps soft dark brown sugar
1 tsp tamarind juice

Garnish
Chopped fresh coriander leaves

---

1. Crush the cardamom pods with the side of a knife and remove the seeds.

2. Place the coriander seeds, caraway seeds, cardamom and cloves in a wok and dry-fry for 1 minute, tossing frequently to prevent burning. Remove from the heat.

3. Mix the fried seeds, chillies, garlic, lemon grass, spring onion, ginger, nutmeg and oil. Pound together in a pestle and mortar.

4. Slice the beef into 1.25×5 cm/½×2 inch chunks.

5. Heat the oil for shallow-frying in a wok and fry the potato and onion wedges for 5 minutes or until they begin to soften, then remove.

6. Add the meat to the pan and fry until browned. Stir in a quarter of the coconut milk and simmer gently for 30 minutes or until meat is very tender.

7. Remove the meat from the pan with a slotted spoon and set aside. Add the chilli mixture to the pan and boil rapidly for 5 minutes, then blend in the remaining milk.

8. Return the meat, onions and potatoes to the wok. Stir in the sugar and tamarind juice. Cook gently for 20 minutes. Garnish with coriander.

Five Spice Pork (See - Krong Moo Ob)

SERVES 4

Serve this delicious, sweet, spicy dish with rice.

PREPARATION: 10 mins
COOKING: 15 mins

680g/1½lbs belly of pork strips
2 tbsps oil
1 tbsp green curry paste, see page 28
2 tbsps fish sauce
1 tbsp light soy sauce
2 tbsps sugar
1 tsp five spice powder
1 tbsp chopped lemon grass

Garnish
Fresh coriander and lime twists

1. Cut the pork strips into 4cm/1½-inch chunks.

2. Heat the oil in a wok and fry the curry paste for 2 minutes, stir in the fish sauce, soy sauce, sugar, five spice powder and lemon grass. Cook for a further 3 minutes.

3. Add the pork to the wok and cook, tossing it

Step 2 Fry the curry paste for 2 minutes, stir in the fish sauce, soy sauce, sugar, five spice powder and lemon grass.

Step 3 Add the pork and cook, tossing it frequently.

frequently, for 10 minutes until pork is cooked.

4. Serve garnished with fresh coriander and lime twists.

Chicken with Chilli and Basil

SERVES 4

Three kinds of basil are used in Thailand. Bai Horapa is the nearest to European basil.
Look out for the other Thai varieties in Oriental food stores.

PREPARATION: 20 mins
COOKING: 20 mins

---

4 chicken quarters
3 large red chillies, seeded and chopped
1 tbsp chopped fresh coriander root and stem
2 cloves garlic, crushed
3 tbsps oil
2 green chillies, sliced
2 tbsps fish sauce
1 tbsp oyster sauce (optional)
Small bunch basil, torn into small pieces

Garnish
Chilli 'flowers'

---

1. Cut the chicken into small pieces using a

Step 1 Cut the chicken into smaller pieces.

Step 4 Return the chicken to the pan add green chillies, fish sauce and oyster sauce.

large sharp knife or meat cleaver.

2. Pound the red chillies, coriander and garlic together in a pestle and mortar.

3. Heat the oil in a wok and fry the chicken until golden and almost cooked. Remove from the pan.

4. Add the chilli paste and fry for a few minutes. Return chicken to the pan and add the green chillies, fish sauce and oyster sauce, if using. Cook over a medium heat for 5-10 minutes or until the chicken is completely cooked.

5. Stir in the basil leaves and serve garnished with chilli 'flowers'.

Prawns in Green Curry Paste

SERVES 2-3

This is the hottest of Thai curries because of the large number of small green Serrano chillies traditionally used.

PREPARATION: 15 mins
COOKING: 10 mins

Green Curry Paste
10 green Serrano or other small chillies, chopped
3 cloves garlic, crushed
2 stems lemon grass, roughly chopped
3 spring onions, chopped
1 tsp grated fresh root ginger
1 tsp coriander seeds
1 tsp caraway seeds
4 whole cloves
1 tsp ground nutmeg
1 tsp shrimp paste
3 tbsps oil

Curry
200ml/7 fl oz thick coconut milk
2 tbsps green curry paste
340g/12oz peeled, raw prawns
1 tbsp fish sauce

Garnish
Lemon rind

---

1. Make the curry paste by placing all the ingredients in a food processor and grinding to a paste. Store in a small jar in the refrigerator until required.

Step 2 Heat a little of the coconut milk in a wok and add the curry paste, boil rapidly for 5 minutes.

2. Heat a little of the coconut milk in a wok and add 2 tbsps of the curry paste, boil rapidly for 5 minutes, stirring frequently, then reduce the heat.

3. Gradually stir in the remaining coconut milk, then add the prawns and fish sauce. Cook gently for about 5 minutes until prawns are cooked. Garnish with lemon rind.

Step 3 Gradually stir in the remaining coconut milk, then add the prawns and fish sauce.

Spicy Steamed Pork with Noodles

SERVES 4

Noodle dishes like this are served as part of the main course or as a snack at any time of the day.

PREPARATION: 20 mins
COOKING: 20 mins

225g/8oz minced pork
1 tsp ground coriander
1 tsp ground cumin
1 tsp ground turmeric
Beaten egg, if needed
1 bunch bok choy or spinach, washed
1-2 tbsps green curry paste, see page 28
1 tsp shrimp paste
140ml/¼ pint thick coconut milk
175g/6oz egg noodles

Garnish
Chopped fresh coriander

---

1. Place the minced pork and ground spices in a food processor and process until very finely chopped. Shape the pork mixture into small balls using damp hands. (If you do not have a food processor, mix the ingredients together and add a little egg to help bind the mixture together.)

2. Tear the bok choy into large pieces and place in a heat-proof dish that will fit into a steamer. Arrange the pork balls on top.

3. Mix together the curry paste, shrimp paste

Step 2 Tear the bok choy into large pieces and place in a heat-proof dish that will fit into a steamer.

Step 3 Mix together the curry paste, shrimp paste and coconut milk and pour over the pork balls.

and coconut milk and pour over the pork balls. Cover and steam for 20 minutes.

4. Meanwhile, cook the noodles as directed on the packet. Mix the noodles together with the pork and bok choy or arrange noodles on a plate and pile the pork mixture on top. Garnish with a sprinkling of chopped coriander leaves.

Thai Fried Rice

SERVES 4-6

Add different fresh vegetables to the rice according to what you have to hand. Serve as an accompaniment or as a meal in itself.

PREPARATION: 15 mins
COOKING: 15 mins

A little oil
1 egg, beaten
1 tbsp thin coconut milk
120g/4oz chicken breasts, skinned and cut into small pieces
120g/4oz raw, peeled shrimps
1 small red or green chilli, seeded and chopped
1 tbsp green curry paste
2 tbsps fish sauce
680g/1½lbs cooked rice
120g/4oz long beans or French beans, cut into 2.5 cm/1-inch lengths
6 spring onions, sliced diagonally

Garnish
Chilli 'flowers'

---

1. Heat a wok and brush with a little oil. Beat together the egg and coconut milk and pour into the wok. Swirl the wok so that the egg coats it, to form a thin omelette.

2. Cook for a minute until just brown on the bottom then flip over and cook the other side.

3. Remove from the wok and allow to cool slightly. Roll up and cut into thin strips.

4. Heat a little more oil in the wok and add the chicken and shrimps. Cook quickly, stirring frequently.

5. Add the chilli, curry paste and fish sauce to the pan and heat until sizzling hot. Stir in rice, beans and spring onions.

6. Reduce heat slightly and cook, stirring constantly, until rice is hot.

7. Pile onto a serving dish and garnish with shredded egg and chilli 'flowers'.

Step 7 Pile onto a serving dish and garnish.

Mixed Vegetable Stir-Fry

SERVES 4

Very fresh vegetables cooked quickly and simply play a large part in Thai cuisine as this dish shows.

PREPARATION: 15 mins
COOKING: 6 mins

Prik Dong
6 red or green chillies
90ml/6 tbsps white wine vinegar

2 tbsps oil
3 cloves garlic, crushed
1 shallot, sliced
90g/3oz each cauliflower and broccoli, divided
    into small florets
1 small red pepper, sliced
120g/4oz mange tout
120g/4oz baby corn cobs
120g/4oz long beans or French beans, cut into
    5 cm/2-inch lengths
2 carrots, peeled and sliced
90g/3oz fresh or canned straw mushrooms
2 tsps light brown sugar
1 tbsp light soy sauce

---

1. Slice chillies diagonally and combine with the vinegar to serve as a dipping sauce for the vegetables.

2. Heat the oil in a wok and add all the vegetables at once.

3. Stir-fry for 4 minutes until vegetables are cooked but still crisp.

4. Stir the sugar into the soy sauce and add to the wok, toss well and serve. Serve with the dipping sauce.

Sautéed Bean Sprouts

SERVES 4

A simple vegetable dish which can be served with a hot dipping sauce if wished or as a foil to a hot curry.

PREPARATION: 5 mins
COOKING: 5 mins

---

2 tbsps oil
8 spring onions, thickly sliced
340g/12oz bean sprouts, rinsed and drained
120g/4oz cooked, peeled prawns (optional)
½ small head of Chinese cabbage, shredded
1 tbsp fish sauce

---

1. Heat the oil in a wok until sizzling then add the spring onions, bean sprouts and prawns, if using. Stir-fry for 1-2 minutes.

2. Add the Chinese cabbage and toss over a high heat for about 1 minute or until just beginning to wilt.

3. Stir in the fish sauce and serve immediately with a dipping sauce of your choice.

Step 2 Add the Chinese cabbage and toss over a high heat.

Step 3 Stir in the fish sauce and serve immediately.

Coconut and Banana Pancakes

SERVES 4

These coconut pancakes filled with a tangy lime and banana filling are delicious served warm or cold.

PREPARATION: 15 mins, plus 20 mins standing
COOKING: 15 mins

120g/4oz rice flour
Pinch of salt
2 eggs
280ml/½ pint thin coconut milk
Green food colouring, optional
30g/1oz shredded or desiccated coconut

Filling
Grated rind of ½ lime
2 tbsps lime juice
1 tsp sugar
1 tbsp shredded or desiccated coconut
2 bananas

Oil for frying

---

1. Place the flour and the salt in a mixing bowl and make a well in the centre. Drop in the eggs and a little of the milk.

2. Using a wooden spoon beat well, slowly incorporating the flour until you have a smooth, thick paste.

3. Gradually beat in the remaining milk. Stir in a few drops of food colouring. Allow to stand for 20 minutes.

4. Just before using the batter, stir in the coconut.

5. Meanwhile, make the filling. Mix together the lime rind, juice, sugar and coconut. Slice the bananas and toss in the mixture.

6. To cook the pancakes, heat a little oil in a 20.5 cm/8-inch heavy-based frying pan. Pour off excess oil. Spoon about 60ml/4 tbsps of batter into the pan and swirl to coat the pan. Cook for about 1 minute until the underside is golden.

7. Flip or toss pancake over and cook other side. Slide the pancake out of the pan and keep warm. Repeat until all the batter is used. Fill pancakes with bananas and serve immediately.

Thai Fruit Platter with Coconut Sauce

SERVES 4

Usually a simple Thai meal will finish with fresh fruit. Here we serve a selection of fruit with a simple coconut sauce.

PREPARATION: 30 mins

Selection of Thai Fruit such as:
Lychees
Rambutans
Mango
Pineapple
Watermelon
Honeydew melon
Papaya
Star fruit
Bananas

Coconut Sauce
175ml/6 fl oz thick coconut milk
60g/2oz caster sugar

1. Prepare the fruit; peel lychees or rambutans, starting at the stem end.

2. Cut the mango in half either side of the large central stone, peel and slice the flesh into fingers.

3. Cut the pineapple into wedges, peeled if wished.

4. Cut the melons and papaya in half and discard the seeds. Peel and slice.

Step 2 Cut mango in half and slice into fingers.

Step 4 Peel and slice melon and papaya, discarding the seeds.

5. Slice the star fruit.

6. Cut the banana diagonally into chunks and toss in lemon juice.

7. Arrange the fruit on a serving platter.

8. Make the sauce by combining the coconut milk and sugar. Pour over the fruit or serve in a bowl or jug.

Sticky Rice with Mango and Star Fruit

SERVES 4

Sweet, glutinous rice is served in many forms as a dessert in Thailand. This delicious version is served with mango and star fruit.

PREPARATION: 10 mins, plus overnight soaking
COOKING: 30 mins, plus 15 mins standing

225g/8oz glutinous or sticky rice
420ml/¾ pint thick coconut milk
90g/3oz sugar
Pinch of salt
1 mango
1 star fruit

1. Soak the rice overnight in cold water.

2. Line the top of a steamer with muslin. Drain the rice and place in the steamer, cover and steam for 25 minutes. The rice will be just tender but not fully cooked.

3. Combine the coconut milk, sugar and salt in a saucepan and heat gently. Stir in the steamed rice and simmer for 2 minutes.

Step 2 Drain the rice and place in the steamer, cover and steam for 25 minutes.

4. Remove from the heat, cover and leave to stand for 15 minutes. The rice will continue to cook in this time.

5. Cut the mango in half as close to the large central stone as possible. Remove the peel, and slice. Slice the star fruit.

6. Arrange the fruit and rice attractively on serving dishes.

Index